Vocabulary *Tales* ™

five senses words

P9-DMD-875

I Love Popcorn!

by Maria Fleming
illustrated by Bill Basso

SCHOLASTIC INC.

New York • Toronto • London • Auckland • Sydney
Mexico City • New Delhi • Hong Kong • Buenos Aires

Designed by Maria Lilja
ISBN-13: 978-0-545-08872-5 • ISBN-10: 0-545-08872-0
Copyright © 2009 by Scholastic Inc.
All rights reserved. Printed in China.

SCHOLASTIC, VOCABULARY TALES™, and associated logos are trademarks and/or registered trademarks of Scholastic Inc.

First printing, January 2009

12 11 10 9 8 7 6 5 4 3 2 1   9 10 11 12 13 14/0

Popcorn! Oh, popcorn! I love you a bunch!
You're so fun to make. You're so fun to munch.

KEY WORD: **gaze**

Simple Definition: to look at something with wonder

Sample Sentence: I could *gaze* at the full moon all night long.

My eyes love to **gaze** at the magical sight
of those small, golden kernels turning fluffy and white.

3

Popcorn! Oh, popcorn! I love the loud sound of your **noisy** popping and hopping around.

Pop! Pop! Pop! You **burst** as you fly.
You make my ears think of the Fourth of July.

You smell super great. When I **sniff** you, oh boy!
You make my mouth water. You bring my nose joy.

KEY WORD: scent

Simple Definition: the way something smells

Sample Sentence: The *scent* of a skunk makes me hold my nose.

Your wonderful **scent** sends me floating up high on a big popcorn cloud in a buttery sky.

Popcorn! Oh, popcorn! I do love you so.
I dream of white popcorn falling like snow.

I catch you and toss you. You are light as fluff.
Each piece that I touch feels bumpy and **rough**.

> **KEY WORD: flavor**
>
> **Simple Definition:** the way something tastes
>
> **Sample Sentence:** I love the sweet *flavor* of raisins.

Your taste is so yummy—your **flavor** so good.
Popcorn, I'd eat you all day if I could.

Popcorn for breakfast! Popcorn for dinner!
On a sandwich at lunch, popcorn's a winner!

11

KEY WORD: senses

Simple Definition: what our bodies use to find out about the world; our five senses are sight, sound, smell, taste, and touch

Sample Sentence: My *senses* tell me that a lemon looks yellow and tastes sour.

Your sight, your sound, your smell, taste, and touch—all of my **senses** love you so much.

Popcorn! Oh, popcorn! You're the best snack I know.
I can't wait to eat you. Hey! Where did you go?

Meaning Match

Listen to the definition. Then go to the WORD CHEST and find a vocabulary word that matches it.

1 to break open or explode

2 bumpy

3 to smell something

4 to look at something with wonder

5 what our bodies use to find out about the world

6 the way something tastes

7 the way something smells

8 loud

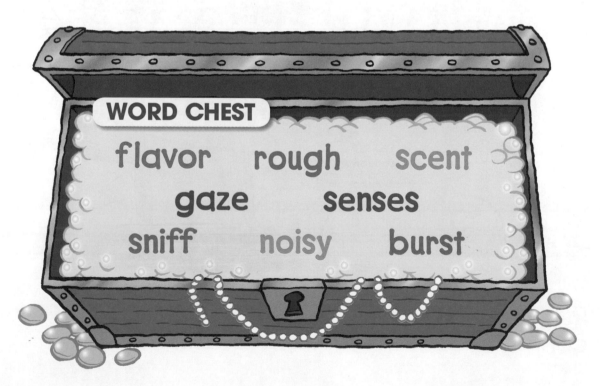

WORD CHEST

flavor   rough   scent

gaze   senses

sniff   noisy   burst

Answers: 1. burst 2. rough 3. sniff 4. gaze 5. senses 6. flavor 7. scent 8. noisy

Vocabulary Fill-ins

Listen to the sentence. Then go to the WORD BOX and find the best word to fill in the blank.

WORD BOX

noisy	sniff	gaze	scent
senses	rough	burst	flavor

1. Brian loved to _____ at the beautiful sunset.

2. What is your favorite _____ of ice cream?

3. Your _____ tell you that snow looks white and feels cold.

4. My nose loves the _____ of bread baking.

5. My parents do not like the _____ sound of my drums.

6. When I _____ the air, I smell the stinky garbage.

7. This shell feels _____ on the outside and smooth on the inside.

8. We watched the fireworks _____ into colors in the sky.

Answers: 1. gaze 2. flavor 3. senses 4. scent 5. noisy 6. sniff 7. rough 8. burst

Vocabulary Questions

Listen to each question. Think about it. Then answer.

1 What is a **scent** you like? What is one you do not like?

2 What do you like to **gaze** at? Tell about it.

3 Which **senses** do you use when you are walking in the rain? Which ones do you use when you go to the supermarket?

4 Pretend someone is making pizza. **Sniff** the air. Talk about what you smell.

5 What things sound **noisy**?

6 Have you ever watched fireworks **burst** in the air? Talk about what you saw and heard.

7 What things feel **rough** when you touch them?

8 What is your favorite ice-cream **flavor**?

Extra: Can you think of some more five senses words? Make a list.